Notice To Readers

This book is intended as a reference volume only. It is not a medical manual. The information contained in this book was written to help readers make informed decisions about their sexual practices and about health issues associated with sexuality. It was not designed as a substitute for any treatment that may have been prescribed by your personal physician. If you suspect that you have a medical problem, see a competent physician to discuss your concerns.

Table of Contents

What is Your Erotic Code?

My mother just doesn't get it! For my birthday she gave me a buckskin jacket, with fringe . . . When I complained, she said, "Wait a minute. I heard you tell your friends how hard it is to find a leather top!"

Eddie Sarfaty, gay comedian

Overall, we live in a sexually illiterate society. Jokes like the one about Eddie's mother symbolize our naiveté about what to call many sexual interests, let alone what they mean. Gays, bisexuals, and straights are given little permission to explore all of their sexuality, including their erotic interests, fantasies, and behaviors that some may consider out of the norm. Your sexual behavior should *not* be ruling you, particularly if they are taking you to unhealthy places. Most people, gay and straight alike, don't know if their fantasies and behaviors are healthy or not. While gay men are more inclined to act out their desires and fantasies more candidly than their heterosexual counterparts, still they remain confused as to what's truly positive and self-affirming.

Therapists are typically uncomfortable talking to their clients about sexuality, mostly because they haven't been trained in working with sex and sexuality nor have worked on exploring their own sexual issues. In J. C. Duffy's comic *Go Fish*, a client and therapist are talking with each other. "There are things I keep hidden from you, Dr. Floyd," the client admits. To which Dr. Floyd responds, "And I want you to know how much I appreciate that, Mr. Pendleton."

Believe it or not, more than 80 percent of all therapists feel like Dr. Floyd when it comes to their clients' sexual confessions. Most therapists are *not* trained in sexuality or sexual health. We are *all* still pioneering this path and all too many psychotherapists still have a low comfort level. If sexuality has been explored much at all, it's from a negative perspective exploring sexual abuse, sexual trauma, and negative messages received about sexuality during one's formative years. An increasing amount of literature is recently coming from a sex- positive place, describing the benefits of understanding your erotic map.

We all have an erotic code. Your erotic code consists of sexual fantasies and sexual interests that turn you on and help you reach orgasm. Here are the questions you will be able to answer from reading this book.

- What is *your* erotic code?
- What can you learn about yourself from your erotic code?
- Is it standing in the way of finding a relationship?

The easiest way to know your erotic code is to think about your peak erotic sexual interests and core erotic themes. In other words, what is the main sexual fantasy you have that gets you off? That is your peak erotic experience. Do you have a few fantasies and desires that bring you to orgasm? Then that is your core erotic themes. What sexual desires and fantasies do you *most admire* or *dislike*? Your peak erotic experiences and fantasies have coded information about you that can help you understand yourself better.

In other words, you have a nonsexual narrative that

exists in your sexual interests and preferences. When you *crack the erotic code* you will learn much more about yourself and your identity. It is like interpreting a dream to discover what is going on with you unconsciously. That is what we will do in this book.

There's a saying that you can tell a lot about a person by knowing who his friends are. Well, if you understand your sexual fantasies and desires, you'll learn a lot about yourself as a person. Sexual fantasies are not separate from, but a result of your psychological makeup—a part of you, an extension of your psyche.

Sexual behaviors and fantasies are an extension of our inner core, windows into another facet of who we are. Whatever gives you the greatest pleasure sexually is information about you. It's telling a story, not necessarily on a conscious level. Regardless of what type of fantasies you enjoy, it's helpful to translate fantasies into reality, albeit in nonsexual ways. You'll find aspects of yourself that you've been seeking all along.

For example, if a client has sexual fantasies of role-playing daddy–boy fantasies, I suggest that he explore his relationships with the important, influential men in his life, starting with his father and/or father figures. Why do people get into topping, bottoming, rimming, fisting, oral and anal sex, and all the other variations? Why do people enjoy fantasies about dominance-submission, humiliation, and fetishes, to name just a few. What about gay men who get off on converting straight men to gay or convincing them to be sexual with you?

Oftentimes a psychological meaning is trying to express itself in the sexual realm. Knowing your erotic code can help you understand yourself more. Otherwise, this information from your personal erotica goes into the darkness, where it sees the light of day rarely, if ever. Without bringing your erotic moments out of the darkness, you will not be experiencing much sexual freedom or choice about what you are doing and want to be doing erotically.

This is not about pathologizing sexual fantasies and interests. It is about understanding them and perhaps enjoying them more fully.

Some fantasies should not be acted on nor does an individual always want to act on them all.

Sexual fantasies and arousal templates are formed with a positive intent. In his book *Arousal: The Secret Logic of Sexual Fantasies*, Michael Bader writes, "my theoretical and clinical approach to sexuality is an affirmative one, viewing sexual fantasy and arousal as resulting from an unconscious attempt to *solve* problems and not, as many psychoanalysts would have it, recreate them."

Here, in the sexual realm, is where individuals and couples can get stuck. Those who contact me for help with their sex lives—couples, particularly—inevitably learn that before they can improve themselves through therapy, they have to learn the nonsexual meanings of their sexual problems.

Some enter relationships with an existing sexual dysfunction— abuse, out-of-control sexual behaviors, physiological dysfunctions, and other problems—that cause the relationship to suffer. Or the couple's relationship itself can create sexual conflicts for the individuals involved, which express themselves through their sexual interactions. Whatever the case, this book will help you explore your own sexual interests more skillfully and thoroughly.

Most buried and suppressed parts of you don't stay that way. Your unconscious is going to knock on the door of your consciousness repeatedly until it gets let out. Until then, it will communicate in code and your work to discover yourself and your erotic code is to decipher the message. Sexual fantasies usually have some unconscious intent that isn't even sexual at all. I learned this over time through treating clients with sexual compulsivity and sexual abuse survivors whose best recovery was based on their understanding the secret logic underneath their sexual fantasies, behaviors, and preferences.

Sexual Fantasies and Integrity

Sexual fantasies allow us to set integrity aside and are often politically incorrect. Things we would never do or say in reality we get to do in our fantasies. Paying careful attention to your sexual desires, erotic needs, and sexual fantasies can learn a great deal about what you're looking for in a partner and want to receive in a relationship. The details of your sexual fantasies don't matter as much as their themes— an important distinction, lest you get lost looking at the details and not be able to see the forest for the trees. Following the themes is like interpreting a dream. The details seem silly, but the symbolism is full of information about you. Whether you have healthy or unhealthy sexual desires, fantasies, or behaviors, it is for your benefit to understand what they represent for you.

As Guy Kettelhack writes in *Dancing Around the Volcano*, "sexual symptoms and fixations are the psyche's energetic and ingenious attempts to cure itself—to give itself what it craves." That is, sexual fantasies and erotic desires are not pathological, but a form of self-help—erotic blueprints that can help you discover yourself, along with the right partner for you.

Our sexual fantasies and erotic templates are like fairy tales: unconscious attempts to adapt and resolve unpleasant and unwanted childhood memories. Bader goes on to say that "we construct particular sexual fantasies and sexual preferences that negate self-denigrating beliefs and feelings, thus allowing sexual excitement to emerge. In order to feel aroused, we temporarily transform ourselves from frogs to princes and princesses. Sexual fantasies undo rejections, turn helplessness into power, redeem feelings of unworthiness, and stamp out even the slimmest vestiges of depression. For just a few moments, just long enough to have an orgasm . . . the ordinary person with dreams of grandeur—imagines him- or herself to be sexually powerful."

The guy seeking out Daddies might be looking for a father figure. There's nothing intrinsically wrong with that unless he's looking for someone to take care of him so that he needn't be accountable for his own life. As a child, he may not have had a father in his life or the father he had was weak, passive, or abusive. A partner cannot make up for what you didn't get as a child; seeking this out in the non-sexual realm could therefore lead to relational problems. In sexual fantasy and play, however, this desire can be satisfied on a temporary basis. That is the cleverness of erotic moments.

Another guy may get aroused by twinks because he came out late and longs to recapture his own youth. His driver's license says he's in his late thirties or older, but in "gay years," he's still in his early twenties. And he may find that while sexually erotic, a true relationship with a guy that young is not effective or even possible. The answer might then be to recapture his youth with a younger partner but without the enormous age difference. He might find other ways to recapture his youth outside the relationship as well. His self-help work, in this case, is to find ways to recapture his youth and mourn for those lost younger years.

If you asked a hundred different men about their sexual fantasies and preferences, you'd get a hundred different answers— many *quite* different. Certain things—even trivial ones—may be important in arousing one man, whereas the same fantasy might turn off the next guy.

That is because everyone's history, childhood, and socialized imprints are different.

Each of us has his own erotic thumbprint. Later, they become the erotic blueprints for arousal, cleverly reenacting to the original disturbing event, this time with a happy ending.

Unfortunately, some fantasies do not translate into reality. If you let yourself be ruled by sexual fantasy instead of being in control of it, it can interfere with finding a partner and entering a relationship.

The Case of Aaron

A good example is a heterosexual male I saw who was about to be married when he came into some legal trouble. Aaron was arrested for approaching adult women in mall parking lots, flashing them with his erect penis, making gestures with his tongue, then getting in his car and speeding away. One upset woman took down his license plate and quickly called the police. Arrested, he admitted to this sexual behavior. He was puzzled as well as ashamed of it and couldn't figure out why he was doing this. To me, he admitted to having done it for some time— and increasingly more often since his engagement and upcoming wedding. Now he faced the shame of telling his fiancée what he had done and the risk of losing her.

Aaron continued in therapy. In looking into his past, we discovered that his mother had been very dominant and controlling while his father was passive and distant. There were older sisters and he was the youngest child and only son. His mother acknowledged and validated his sisters but silenced both my client and his father. If Aaron made any attempts to voice his thoughts, the females would tell him to be quiet. He felt stifled and emasculated.

His sexual fantasies and desires had resolved these feelings by showing these anonymous women what a "man" he was. His tongue gestures let her know he could use his mouth and could pleasure her with it, whereas his family hadn't wanted him to open his mouth to talk and basically gagged him. The women he flashed were stand-ins for his mother and sisters.

His work now, determined by the erotic impulses that we uncovered, was to assert himself more with the women in his life. It turned out (not surprisingly) that his fiancée was opinionated and had a dominant side. Aaron had given her what she wanted and subordinated his own needs—but resented it. Many times he silenced himself and blamed her for it. At work, with female superiors and co-workers, he did the same thing, returning to the scene of the crime by recreating his family dynamics. His sexuality was telling him, "You need to express yourself and your masculinity to women," and channeled it through his sexual behavior by his exhibitionism.

Aaron did, in fact, assert himself more to his wife, and their relationship improved. He read men's studies books and healed his masculinity by embracing it more. His wife had difficulty with this at first but did adjust. His mother and sisters, however, were not receptive when he made the same attempts with them. So Aaron distanced himself from them and built a stronger relationship with his father.

Ultimately, although the thought of showing his penis to unexpecting women still aroused him, he no longer did so. His erotic fantasies no longer ruled him; he had mastered them.

Not surprisingly, Aaron's sexual behavior increased

since his becoming engaged. His unconscious was reaching backward in time to when his dependency needs were highest and he was attached to women who humiliated and emasculated him. His sexual behavior was trying to give him long-delayed resolution for his childhood resentment with the women in his family. Luckily, he found the help to do it, otherwise, his sexual acting-out would have caused further problems, especially in his marriage.

As sex and relationship therapist, as well as author Esther Perel, writes, "tell me how you were loved as a child and I will tell you how you make love as an adult". I couldn't agree more.

All sexual fantasies are healthy, though some—like Aaron's— should never be acted on because they might put the one who has them (or someone else) at risk. Some men discover, for example, that sex with sex workers is a form of "paying for love." As children, they weren't loved or loved enough by their caregivers. Other men feel compelled to take orders, to be dominated and spanked in an effort to be disciplined in ways they never were as children. Others want to dominate and be in charge since they often feel helpless and powerless in life. Some like to be humiliated by golden showers, being spit on, and verbally abused, possibly because they struggle with maintaining a sense of pride in themselves. This doesn't mean that you have to stop your fantasies or change the desires or behaviors they play out. It does mean that if you want to feel more powerful and take more pride in your life, find ways to be loved without always paying for it and make an impact on others in your relationships.

So much of porn—gay and straight—centers on rape fantasies: the hot military/police/boss/coach/teacher or another guy in authority who forces himself onto another man, with both ultimately enjoying it. This allows gay men to feel accepted by a dominant masculine man and provides them with a way to feel good about what's happening to them. Studies show that a high percentage of heterosexual women have rape fantasies, but this doesn't mean they *want* to be raped. For them, I suspect, it's a way of sexualizing the male dominance and patriarchy in their lives.

Gay porn abounds with fraternity fantasies. During

initiation, the fraternity guys humiliate the pledges, notice the gay guy enjoying himself, and ultimately overpower him—to everyone's sexual and erotic pleasure. Everyone wins. The frat brothers get to stay in charge and dominate, while the gay initiate gets his fraternity brothers' acceptance and the sense of belonging that he's longed for.

There's nothing wrong with that fantasy and nothing wrong with play-acting it out. I want to help clients explore—in a positive way—*why* they've developed that *particular* fantasy. And what about incest stories—which can be found in both gay and straight porn?

Sexual fantasies about family members ensure that attention is paid and connections are made. For example, if a parent was depressed, disengaged, and unavailable during a boy's formative years, then an incest fantasy of a parent being sexual with the adult son fixes this. The sexualized connection of the fantasy lets both parent and adult child experience a tight-knit bond. Also, as Bader points out, you can't be sexually aroused and unhappy at the same time. So again, in this parent-adult child fantasy, everyone is happily turned on. Sadness and longings are banished.

This is a far better explanation for sexual fantasies and arousal than attributing them to pathology and sickness. The human psyche is always looking to repair itself and return to wholeness, so it's not surprising that it would use erotica and the sexual realm as corrective tools.

Emotional Landscape and Attachment

Early attachment and bonding experiences shape your later ability to attach and bond with others. We sex therapists understand that these same attachments and experiences help develop and shape sexual fantasies and preferences in adulthood.

This is not to be confused with sexual orientation—how you identify yourself as gay, lesbian, straight, bisexual, or otherwise. Sexual and romantic orientations are who you are inherently at your core.

Sexual preferences are learned and shaped more by how you were raised and the types of relationships you witnessed in childhood.

Sexual arousal is imprinted, beginning in childhood when your sexual map is determined. We observe and absorb how others love, neglect, or abuse us—and that becomes our "love map," or template for what we seek out for pleasure as adults.

In *Arousal: The Secret Logic of Sexual Fantasies*, Bader

writes, “The unconscious management of psychological safety does not begin with the onset of mature sexual desires. It begins in childhood, almost from the moment of birth. As research now tells us, the newborn baby is wired to form an attachment to its mother. The baby can recognize the mother’s particular voice and face and prefers them over all other voices and faces. Evolution has guaranteed that the baby has the ability and desire to connect to the human being most able to help it survive. Furthermore, our brains and psychological natures are primed to make us love those people who are responsible for our well-being.

We become attached, and we fall in love. Without such attachment, psychological research has shown that babies become frantic, disorganized, and depressed. A secure attachment is crucial to healthy psychological development.”

Attachment to a parent figure is the first crucial stage of development. How you learn to attach and bond sets the stage for your later relationships. It also sets the stage for your later sexual content and fantasies. To crack your erotic code, you must learn who your attachment figures were and how they were with you during this developmental time when you were learning to attach.

- Were your attachment figures smothering, or distant and disengaged?
- Did you feel like you were a burden on your parents?
- Did they grant your wishes, or did you have to grant their wishes?
- Did they allow you your independence growing up, or was that discouraged?

If your parents were unhappy, depressed, and unavailable, and you responded by trying not to upset them or demand too much, then you may be working out these conflicts within your erotic landscape. In *Arousal*, Bader writes about people in sexual fantasies being happy; in the sexual sphere, everyone is pleased—no depressed mother, a "giving" parent, a sense of belonging unlike that which you might have had in your family.

In addition, the needs of gay children and teens are less likely to get met as we are invisible and are not tracked for the gay boys we are. We gay men have also not been allowed to explore our sexuality openly and consciously from the beginning as do our heterosexual counterparts.

Erotic Intelligence

Rather than pathologizing and diagnosing someone as having disturbed sexual thoughts or troubled fantasies, sex therapists reframe this imagery as self-healing and corrective—the client's attempts to resolve and understand his own psychic issues. Line up ten people and ask each one to be honest about what turns him on the most; you're likely to hear ten different answers. And each response will tell you about that man and his history.

It may be difficult for clients to reveal their sexual fantasies and interests in therapy, but once they do, we find plenty of information about them. From those with compulsive sexual behaviors, I've learned that if we can uncover the non-sexual aspects of disguised material or "story," then I can help them a great deal more. Using this lens on even healthy sexual fantasies provides a wealth of information about them.

Healthy Sexuality

Before we can explore sex and sexual preferences, we need to understand healthy versus unhealthy sexuality. In their book *Treating Out of Control Sexual Behaviors: Rethinking Sex Addiction*, sex therapists Doug Braun-Harvey and Michael Vigorito have written the best description I've encountered on what is involved in the dimensions of healthy sexuality. They describe six principles to recognize if your sexual behaviors are healthy or not. The principles are as follows.

1. Consent
2. Non-exploitive
3. Safer Sex
4. Honesty
5. Shared Values
6. Mutually Pleasurable

As you read on, consider whether your sexual desires, fantasies, and behaviors have these healthy principles. If not, that simply means you might want to seek out a therapist who understands how to help you understand them. But if you’re acting out any fantasy that puts you or others at risk in any way, you should seek help immediately.

Sexual Intimacy

Men—gay, bisexual, and straight—often say they can separate sex from love. They can have sex with one person without attaching or wanting anything else and can also have sex with those with whom they fall in love. I once worked with a couple who said that they would either make love or have "throw-me-down" sex—simply gratifying raw sexual needs without affection being a part of it. While not all men are this way, many are quite capable of making this sort of division.

But sexual contact with another guy can get confused with a genuine emotional connection. Many people use sex to fill a void in their lives and to feel wanted, but sexual contact alone is *not* love. While it can help couples stay close to each other and let individuals release their libido, the rest of their relational work needs to happen outside the sexual realm. In other words, even though sexual contact might fulfill your psyche somehow, it's no replacement for the work necessary to attach to a partner and have real love—which isn't easy. Sex offers instant pleasure, but true sexual and romantic intimacy takes work. If you're not doing that work, the relational intimacy is often shallow and superficial.

I often meet clients who were raised in families where affection was not shown outwardly. Often they'll explain away this lack of expression as the "WASP way" or "a German thing" or "the way of the English folk." They'll tell me they never doubted they were—and are— loved by their parents, but were never shown its outward expressions. I begin to teach them that while they logically understand that they're loved, a part of the brain doesn't understand. Lack of demonstrative affection can often make children feel emotionally neglected. These children are starving for direct affection and act out in ways to get it somewhere else. Frequently, there is incest between siblings or sex between cousins and neighborhood kids, as a means of attaining physical affection.

The Case of Todd and Gary

Todd called me for couple's therapy. He and his partner, Gary, had been together eight years, and Todd was feeling unloved. Gary stated he loved Todd very much. But the frequency of sex between them had diminished from twice a week to once a month. Todd saw this as a sign that Gary was falling out of love with him.

When they came in, Gary reported feeling happy with the frequency and amount of sexual activity they did together. Todd felt frustrated with Gary's unwillingness to top for him. Todd was a top himself and mostly enjoyed that, but wanted to bottom at times, but Gary wouldn't do it. Gary said that in the beginning of their relationship he was open to it and actually did top for Gary. But after three years together, when Gary did try to top Todd, he would go limp. So with Gary's permission, Todd found a "fuck buddy" on the side that he would see monthly. Gary seemed truly okay with Todd's activity outside the relationship—in fact, he seemed *too* okay with it. Yet Gary didn't want to be sexual with others outside the relationship: he reported having a much lower libido and less interest in sexual contact. Todd often felt unloved because of Gary's lack of sexual interest in him. One way they negotiated this was for the two of them to have sex with other male couples, igniting sexual energy in Gary and restoring some of the passion between them.

Gary was beginning to feel uncomfortable having sex with these other couples. He wanted to keep what they had just between them and was fine if Todd wanted to keep his fuck buddy. But this made Todd feel even more unloved. Gary said that in general he just didn't have as much interest in sex as Todd did and his desire was lacking. But Todd found this hard to believe as he found cum rags and Kleenexes on Gary's side of the bed and also found websites that Gary was visiting online. Gary admitted that yes, he masturbated, but said that was easy and faster than making time for them to have sex. This hurt Todd even more. When they did have sex together, Todd felt that Gary was forcing himself and that he was not really into it as much as he could be. Gary said when they were sexual, he was into it, but Todd didn't believe him.

Todd was okay with having his fuck buddy outside the relationship. He said he wished Gary were into it because he preferred to keep sex within the relationship. But he understood that Gary wasn't, so he said having a fuck buddy fulfilled his appetite.

Looking into each other's pasts made things clearer. Todd was from a family he described as "WASPy," where not much affection was shown, but he knew he was loved. His father worked quite a bit out of the house, and his stay-at-home mother mostly cared for the house, provided meals, always attended his school and sporting events, and drove him wherever he needed to go. He didn't recall many instances of his mother telling him she loved him and gave him few kisses and hugs. She provided custodial care at best.

When Todd was twelve, a sixteen-year-old cousin fondled him and then had Todd give him oral sex. Todd recalls very much enjoying what he referred to as his "first sexual experience" with another guy. Later, he became very sexual with other boys his age on his street, inviting them to sleep over at his house and then engage in mutual masturbation and oral sex.

Todd learned early on that being sexual with his older cousin felt good, but the truth was that his cousin sexually abused him. Instead, Todd saw it as love, because of the emotional neglect he'd experienced within his family.

Sexual abuse and incest is common in families that

don't show emotion and affection. In fact, most sexual predators can spot children from this type of home and use their craving for love and acceptance to their advantage.

Now, as an adult, he was reenacting his childhood in his relationship with Gary. To get the love he craved, he was going out of the relationship to have sex with other men. It was no accident that he was partnered with Gary. Theirs was a true match. In other words, Todd equated sex with love and with Gary's sexual interest being low this re- enacted Todd's feelings of being unloved.

Now their *real* couples work could begin. I told Todd he'd unconsciously "hired" Gary to rewound him the same way his parents had by not showing love the way that would have felt familiar and fulfilling. Gary was doing so by not showing sexual interest the way Todd wanted it—how he'd learned to feel loved as a boy. But Todd was letting Gary off the hook as he had his parents, by seeking "love" outside the family—which was why he sought sex outside his relationship.

Most couples would feel hopeless, not understanding what to do once they'd figured out this dynamic in their relationship. I recommended that both Gary and Todd stop all outside sexual activity. While gay male couples do manage to have successful open relationships, I sometimes recommend they discontinue all outside sexual activity when they enter therapy if there are sexual problems or a break in the relationship agreement around open relationship contracts so that they can sort out the rupture that has occurred between them.

Once that's fixed, then they can return to their outside activity. It was to Todd's benefit to stay and fight for the monogamous relationship he wanted and to negotiate more for Gary to comply with topping him. This brought up Gary's issues, as I knew it would. This all needed to happen since both Gary and Todd were reenacting issues from their pasts.

Gary's mother and father had a distant relationship and his smothering, engulfing mother turned to Gary for her emotional needs. Gary was a good student with polite friends, but his mother distrusted him. During high school, she made him come home earlier than all of his friends and would smell his breath, not trusting that he hadn't done drugs, even though there were no signs of any chemical use.

So in Gary's unconscious effort to keep Todd from smothering and engulfing him, it made sense that he would keep him at an emotional and sexual distance. In my Imago Relationship Therapy training there is a saying: "What you want most from your partner is hardest for them to give because it's the very thing they need to do for themselves." So it was in Todd's favor to ask Gary for what he wanted and continue his attempts to get his needs met *inside* the relationship (and thus, symbolically, without leaving his "family").

He let Gary off the hook of having to face his issues with his mother. Gary needed someone to demand more closeness so that he could work through learning that intimacy doesn't have to mean being engulfed.

Ultimately, Gary was able to top more for Todd, who no longer felt compelled to go outside their relationship. They left therapy with the understanding that if they did choose to bring in others for sexual play, they would do so knowing it was a choice, not an acting-out of some relationship.

Core Erotic Themes

Jack Morin, author of *The Erotic Mind: Unlocking the Inner Sources of Sexual Passion and Fulfillment*, invites people to explore their peak sexual experiences, favorite masturbation fantasies, and the pornography they choose to read and watch. He argues that examining these things helps you to discern your core erotic theme (CET). This internal blueprint for arousal, Morin says, "transforms old wounds and conflicts into excitation." He goes on to say that "hidden in within your CET is a formula for transforming unfinished emotional business from childhood and adolescence into excitation and pleasure."

Morin believes, as do I, that these internal blueprints are about more than just love: they enter our erotic minds as well. But most people—male and female, gay, bisexual and straight—don't examine their sexual behaviors and fantasies that aren't interfering with their lives. The examples I use in this book come from my therapy practice from clients who are suffering from behaviors and desires they wish they did not have and that they don't like. This doesn't mean, however, that you could not learn more about yourself from the sexual behaviors that you enjoy and like. You can—and will—as you read on.

Pornography Is Today's Sex Education

Culturally, we lack nonsexual rituals and initiations into gay manhood. Our society lacks images of men—particularly gay and bisexual men—touching and expressing affection; gay porn reconciles this lack, if only through sexuality. There isn't any gay sex education in our schools today. Heterosexually married gay men who lack the courage to go to a gay bar or support group find porn, the Internet, and gay apps the easiest, safest way to explore their sexuality. Pornography can be a source of recreational pleasure and a rite of passage into gay manhood, but also a source of pain that interferes with your life.

Having pornography serve as one's initiation into gay manhood can feed a man's impression that being gay is forbidden and underground. Sneaking around looking at gay porn on the Internet can make him feel shameful, but also add to the excitement.

We gay men are negatively sexually scripted and shaped by cultural, societal, and religious messages.

I discovered that some positives occurred by gay men

telling me that it helped them identify what their sexual and erotic interests are. They were able to sort what they liked and didn't like through watching pornography.

Bathhouses

In my opinion, anonymous sex at the baths can be a great means to making connections with other gay men and sexually experiment and explore. You can dramatize what is going on in your head by acting it out with men at the baths. For the most part, no true intimacy is transpiring, and all the men are in a very self-absorbed state of mind in terms of selfishly getting their sexual needs met and objectifying each other but that is what makes the baths hot and exciting for many men who go. Even those who go there to “please” or “serve” other men are really there to meet their own sexual needs. It is not necessarily a place to make deep connections.

Recreationally, there’s nothing wrong with going to the baths if you see it for what it is—a sexual thrill, a quickie, and release. For someone who doesn’t have a partner or it not interested in one, the baths may provide touch, sexual release, quick and immediate contact, and pseudo-connection—as well as offering an area for play and fantasy fulfillment. If that’s all you want, then the baths provide an excellent forum for that, as long as you practice safe sex.

Most interestingly from a cultural perspective, bathhouses are acknowledged and frequented in our gay culture, yet stigma is attached to admitting that one frequents them. As out and open as going to bathhouses seems to be—even to straights—it's impolite to talk about it. Whether at parties or and when dating, many (if not most) gay men will never admit to going. I've heard both clients and friends tell me that they'd never date a man who goes to the baths, even though they may have gone themselves.

Gay Dating and Sex Apps

Gay dating and sex apps such as Grindr and Scruff are the places we make sexual connections these days. I talk more about this in my first book, *10 Smart Things Gay Men Can Do To Improve Their Lives*. Sexual connections remind us that we exist. Growing up as gay men, we're taught not only that we don't belong, but that we don't exist—by not seeing ourselves portrayed very much in the media or in print unless in a caricature or cartoon fashion like Mitch and Cam on *Modern Family* or Jack on *Will and Grace*. From childhood on, we're not mirrored or acknowledged for being gay little boys. The gay dating apps and bathhouse are ways to remind ourselves that we're still "there" without having to exert hardly any emotional or mental work.

Taking My Breath Away

The Case of Carter

Sexual hookups fulfill our sense of belonging. As gay little boys we not only weren't seen by heterosexist culture but we didn't see each other. Gay dating apps are a way to feel seen and get a sense of belonging.

As I said in the beginning, you can tell a lot about a person by their sexual fantasies and erotic interests. This was the case with Carter.

Carter came into therapy troubled that he was almost forty and never had a healthy relationship with another man. He was able to have hookups and quick sexual encounters but dating was almost absent for him. He didn't know what was wrong with him or with the gay male community, but something was wrong in his mind.

He had come out in his early twenties and in a short time had fully accepted himself as a gay man. He told me he was well read on gay topics and attended gay events either with friends or alone without anxiety. He was a handsome man with a nice build and everything that most gay men would find attractive. Then why was he having trouble attracting them? He couldn't see it at all.

Carter had a nice personality and healthy outlook on life. On the outside, everything seemed normal. His childhood, however, was anything but. In my initial assessment of him, I asked about his sexual behavior. He told me he liked getting on Grindr for his sexual and dating needs both locally and when he traveled.

I explained that the more he was willing to share with me about his family history and his sexual interests, the more I could help him.

As a sex and relationship therapist, what I know is that we are drawn to familiar love and familiar sex. How we are raised in our families and our socialization shapes the people we are attracted to and the erotic interests that we have.

He began opening up to me about his family, social, and sexual history. As Carter grew more comfortable, he was able to fully express his experiences:

"I like to get on Grindr and have guys pursue me. I like to send them a dick pic so they can see how big I am. Even soft I have a nice- sized cock that hangs well. I enjoy reading the responses from other guys when they see it both hard and soft. It's very exciting to me when they are surprised that I'm as big and round as I am.

Then we hook up and they see my cock. We never say a wordto each other. I stand up and he puts my hard cock in his mouth. If he looks up at me, I look away. I don't like eye contact. Then I startto face-fuck him. I grab his hair and his ears sometimes. I literally like to rape his mouth. What I like most is to shove my cock down his throat so far that momentarily he can't breathe. If he chokes, I don't care. Then I pull back, and they gasp for air sometimes. That arouses me even more. I'll let him catch his breath and then go right back to face-fucking him. I like it best when they're in this position and let me do that to them without protest.

Then I turn around and shove my ass in their face and have them rim me. I position us so that I can literally sit on the guy's face and force my ass over his nose and mouth, and I sit there, knowing he momentarily cannot breathe or make a sound. Then I decide to let him up and again he gasps for air. Then I turn around and come on his face or body and leave him there".

Direct and raw as this story is, it took Carter an entire year to tell it all to me. He was very embarrassed and often wept while recounting it. He admitted how very out of character it was for him to be so cold and aggressive with the men at the baths because otherwise he never dominated or was this harsh with people. In fact, one thing that frustrated him most about others was when they acted dominant and aggressive toward him!

Returning to the Scene of the Crime

When I work with clients that are struggling with sexual issues I try to crack that erotic code and see what crime they are trying to solve that was committed in their past.

Together we started to decipher the coded message—the theme of his sexual script—to understand what he was acting out. As in the expression *You take my breath away*, I told him that sexually he had found a way of literally "taking a guy's breath away." Carter's ultimate fantasy was the moment when the guy couldn't breathe. Not that he wanted the man to show discomfort, protest, or even be humiliated; he simply wanted the guy to be willingly suffocated and smothered by his erect penis and buttocks. At these moments, he realized, he became the other guy's *whole world*. When the man couldn't breathe, he could think of nothing else except when Carter was ready to give him air.

Later, in talking about Carter's childhood, we would learn how he never felt precious to his parents or anything close to "taking their breath away" as a revered and honored son.

Carter had no idea why this should excite him, nor had he ever thought about figuring it out. He just knew he liked it and didn't think much about it after leaving the guy. Nor did he like to do this with guys he dated. It was only a turn-on for him with anonymous men he met on gay dating and sex apps.

Carter was the middle child of three boys. His father was passive and introverted, his mother self-absorbed and narcissistic. His mother was a misandrist (someone who hates males). She talked at length about "how men used others as sexual objects and only thought with their dicks." He regularly witnessed his mother's disgust and contempt for male sexuality. She was determined to create good "feminized boys," Carter said to me.

He talked about his never-ending, unsuccessful attempts to please his mother. Even when he felt he'd done exactly as she wished, she was never satisfied. Parents should have a certain amount of awe for their children, hold them in reverence and see them as precious. This was not the case in Carter's family. Carter's mother used her children to please *her* and didn't see that it was her duty to please *them*. His introverted father didn't stand up for males when his mother talked about them in derogatory ways, so Carter was imprinted with the idea that men were no good and ineffectual like his father and the men his mother complained of. So he had become her "bad boy" sexually, showing off to everyone and defying his mother's wishes, while also being the center of many men's attention.

It made sense that Carter's erotic coding, in its corrective efforts, sought out men who saw him as virile and able to provide them pleasure—unlike how he was able to with his mother and father. The sexual contact provided a pseudo-connection and through sexual pleasure, Carter was able to satisfy these men. He wasn't successful in pleasing his parents, so in his sexual conquests he returned to the scene of the crime—and solved it. Yet his parents' original neglect and invisibility weren't corrected by this momentary sexual acting-out; thus, Carter created a cycle of meeting anonymous men through dating and sex apps repeatedly. In the long run, the crime continued to be perpetrated on Carter himself.

In his search for boyfriends, Carter kept meeting men whom he described as self-absorbed. These men wanted him to attach to them, but wouldn't attach back to him. Guys like this rarely asked Carter about himself and this would enrage him—which made sense since this was a close imitation of his parents. He sought out familiar love as we all do and picked partners who were similar to the parent he had the most difficult and unresolved issues with. In Carter's case, it was his mother.

His anger was really at his parents, not so much at these men. Other guys might date these men once and never see them again, but Carter would keep seeing them over a period of months. Once we decoded the themes of his sexual script, Carter was able to deal with the negative messages about males he suffered as a child by his mother's inappropriate preoccupation with males behaving badly sexually and their "bad intentions." He also started to face the emotional neglect he'd felt in his family. He didn't *take his parents' breath away* as so many cherished children do. When he was also unable to find male partners whose breath he took away, he resolved it in the sexual realm. But that was not enough. Now his work was about finding a sense of belonging around others, particularly gay men, instead of trying to find it only through sexual hookups. He would look for a man who would love and revere him.

Lost Tweakends

Crystal meth and sexual behavior often go together. In his book *Tweakers*, Frank Sanello reports that crystal meth is the drug of choice for its users because it "artificially rewards the user's brain by releasing torrents of dopamine and other neurotransmitters." Elevated levels of dopamine provide craving for sex; what better way to be reassured that you exist than with high levels of dopamine causing exhilaration, increased energy, and sexual desire? You only have to take the drug and you are there! But like NutraSweet, "Tina" only tastes and looks like the real thing.

Gay men get the message that we don't belong. We have no mirrors of ourselves in view and so early on we learn that "officially" we don't exist. Is it any wonder that drugs and sex can become a way of feeling alive, of achieving a sense of belonging? In violence toward the self, it provides a pseudo-sense of belonging, much as it does in people suffering from trauma. Our trauma is that we are invisible, even to each other, and we use sex and drugs to perpetuate our invisibility.

How many “lost tweakends” will you suffer before you stop, find yourself, and direct your dependency needs into good romantic or friendly heart-to-heart relationships? You deserve what you were seeking to begin with—real live connection, attention, and affection.

Bodily Harm

The gym is yet another place where we have felt rejection and trauma around changing and showering with other men, without permission to stare. While some sexuality and cruising do go on in health clubs, the gyms have become a serious place for gay men to get their bodies into shape—but not always for the right reasons. Gay men build their bodies to look like Warriors, but again, integrity is an issue. How they look on the outside doesn't reflect who they are on the inside.

In *Dancing Around the Volcano*, Kettelhack writes, "There's an odd disjunction in much of gay male experience: while the gym has become as sacred and important an experience to gay men as the church is to nuns, few gay men I've talked to have much physical self- acceptance. The Body, as purveyed by The Gym, is like an Armani suit that takes money and untold hours of discipline to earn. It is something acquired—something almost external to the being acquiring it." I couldn't agree more.

Often when I see these gay men—ripped, buff, and hunky—I have to remind myself that these are my gay brothers, not the bullies who intimidated and humiliated me in school. Yet that's how these gay men present themselves. Many of them have "stay away from me" attitudes and look as though they'll shun me or look down on me if I speak to them. On a recent gay cruise I was on, one man said that he purposely stayed away from those "Armani suits" around the pool, out of fear they would reject him. Finally, he decided not to let this intimidate him and he took his imperfect body to sit by the pool anyway.

In many ways, gay men who are into working out are finding their sense of belonging at the gym. As teenagers, we often were not part of the club of those other aggressive boys who intimidated us.

Working out at the gym is a way to recapture those lost years searching for the masculine archetypes we weren't allowed to claim; but becoming *supermales* is only a continuation of what we've always done to compensate: to overachieve.

It wouldn't be fair to say that all of those who go to the gym to perfect their bodies have that attitude and separate themselves from other gay men. But so many do, and the shame of it is that we're doing to ourselves what was done to us. This is a common response to being victimized. If you are bullied, intimidated, and humiliated, and put in a subservient role, one way to overcome it is to become the bully. Still, you are not in a position of power, but rather powerlessness.

But what about those who choose not to or cannot have bodies like these men?

Unhung Heroes: Men with Small Penises

One of the worst shadows we men have is how we feel about our penis sizes. And I have heard gay men say that this matters in terms of partner selection and sexual satisfaction.

There isn't much written nor talked about regarding men with small penises. The March 2005 issue of *OUT* includes Erik Piepenburg's article "Is Small Beautiful?" which focuses on gay men with small penises. The journalist interviewed Robert Woodworth, a fifty-nine-year-old gay man and director of Institutional Services at New York's Lesbian, Gay, Bisexual and Transgender Community Center. Woodworth began an ongoing series of discussions about gay men and their penises, which led to a four-week support group for gay men who feel that theirs are small.

Bravo to these men! They are truly unhung heroes, willing to disclose their genital size and come out of their fly, as well as the closet. What pressure they must feel as men—particularly in the gay community—where penis size is talked about so relentlessly and so judgmentally, as if it were a measure of the whole man. I'm sure there are many, many jokes about this support group. When I was researching the article, one colleague asked me, "Is it a small support group?" Another colleague inquired, "How long will your article be?" Snicker all you want, but the real joke is on all of us men since such remarks make many of us feel self-conscious about our size. When I hear any gay man make a small penis comment—particularly in front of others in my gay men's groups or workshops—I cringe to think of those insecure men who might feel bad or those who just worry about their size in general.

What Is Too Small—Really?

The Kinsey Institute set the standard for penis size in the 1960s. Alfred Kinsey and his merry men studied American college-age men and found that 80 percent of fully erect penises measured between five and seven inches long, with most falling in the six- to six-and-a half- inch range. But size queens beware! Despite what you might surmise from gay personal ads, less than 1 percent of those erections Kinsey witnessed in the flesh exceeded eight inches. The odds against finding a true nine-incher are a thousand to one, but still considerably better than winning the Lotto. The difference between Internet inches and real-life inches is in the eye of the owner, not the beholder.

But does the rarity of those knitting needles in the haystack make any one of us men feel any better? No! Men are hung in different sizes, widths, directions, and shapes, and each of us is different, whether hard or soft. Some men are showers and some men are growers. Still, at a nude beach or locker room, men with bigger and longer flaccid endowment are more fortunate. They have less to worry about in terms of being judged and found wanting, or hearing snide remarks made about them. Even if their four-inch softie doesn't grow when erect, straight guys in a locker room, bathhouse, or nude beach won't know that. The guy who might boast only one to two inches soft and grow to eight inches hard still feels self-conscious, thinking that when at ease, everyone sees him as too small, even though at attention, he knows he's not.

What we're really talking about here is how much of a man someone is. And we tend to measure masculinity by various standards—by how tall or short he is, how successful, wealthy, athletic, or stoic and so on—all measurements of outward qualities; how sad that is. We need to look more at the inside, evaluating a man by his integrity, responsibility, talents, eloquence, and accountability. Why not measure a man by the size of his heart? That is what real love is all about. That way, you'll wind up with more satisfaction than you've ever dreamed of.

Queer Eye for the Straight Guy

I've identified the cultural phenomenon of gay males seeking "straight acting" gay men because of internalized homophobia and how they're more often looking for masculine acting men. But what about gay men's sexual obsessions with real straight men? I've heard countless clients tell me of their interest in "getting sexual with a straight man" for one night. Some clients talk about wanting to "service" him without reciprocation. Others want him to participate by talking or telling him what to do, while still others want him to lay back and be worshiped. Others want the straight man to humiliate them, while still others want the straight man to suddenly become sexually interested back toward him. Whatever the case, it gives you more information about yourself as there are nonsexual narratives behind each one of these scenarios.

I see sexual fantasies about straight men as sometimes being longings for acceptance by straight men in general or your father. Straight men can be stand-ins for your fathering figures.

In *Arousal*, Bader describes the situation of straight

women sexually attracted to gay men because they're "safe." He writes that these women can become "sexually expressive . . . in a more confident and spontaneous way than they can with straight men . . . because their overtures will not be reciprocated. These are women who have anxieties about being sexual with straight men because they're afraid of being overpowered or rejected." A gay man won't cross the line toward her, making it safe for women to flirt and be sexually aggressive with him without risking rejection since he is gay anyway. If she convinces the gay guy to be sexual with her, Bader states that this is "reassurance that she is *especially* attractive."

Gay men have been wounded, bruised, beaten down, and humiliated by straight men— resulting in straight men, particularly those in a position of authority, being recipients of both positive and negative transferences from gay men. We hear over and over that these men would never accept a fem boy— which many of us have accepted that we are. Because of this, some gay men often fear straight men. As children, we do love these male figures and we want their acceptance; as adults, we sexualize these straight men because it unconsciously offers a way to feel safely and pleasantly attached to them. In the sexual fantasy of pleasing a straight guy, you finally get a chance to make contact with him and get the approval you have always wanted.

Some gay men have fantasies of overpowering straight men— seducing or forcing gay sex onto them. Again, while these fantasies can make for exciting fun, preoccupation with them or acting on them— even with a willing straight male— might interfere with you finding Mr. Right in the long run, if that is in fact what you are looking for. It can also be a distraction from examining your own issues around straight males.

Paying for Love

Although an extreme example, Abe's story is worth telling if your attraction to straight men stands in your way of healthy relationships with men, gay, bisexual and straight.

Abe came to me for depression, worried that he was over thirty- five and never had a significant relationship. He wanted one, but could never make them work. He even knew what the problem was: he was sexually attracted to straight men. In fact, if he thought a man was straight who later turned out to be gay, he'd get turned off. This he identified as internalized homophobia, which in part it was, but also a symptom of something more. He was returning to the scene of some crime with a straight man, as the sexual details of his story would make clear.

Abe always had had fantasies of straight guys wrestling. He'd spend a lot of time watching wrestling on television, then go into his room and masturbate. In middle school, however, he hadn't been interested in wrestling. Outside of the sexual fantasies, it would provoke anxiety and low self-esteem, since he had a smaller build and wasn't very strong or athletic. Abe always masturbated to fantasies of meeting these straight guys, who overpowered him through various wrestling holds. The bigger and more muscular the guys, the better—this was his ultimate fantasy. When he was with gay men, he would use this fantasy to ultimately get himself off. Thus, his fantasy was so strong that it prevented him from truly connecting, which is why he was unable to have healthy relationships with other gay men.

Abe found a website where there were straight-identified male models—sex workers—specifically, those who wrestled and pumped up their bodies. These guys were only interested in letting guys pay them to show off their muscles. Abe would meet them, but they would not allow him to undress or masturbate—only modeled their bodies while Abe watched. They would strip down to briefs, but never get naked, and perform wrestling holds on him. For Abe, this ensured their heterosexuality and turned him on even more. If they even hinted that sex or nudity might be involved, he'd lose interest. His favorite erotic scenarios were of nonsexual contact with a straight male wrestler. He loved the feeling of one being on top of him.

One time, one of the models got him in a wrestling hold and told him, "You're a good boy. You paid me well. You behave well. You deserve the honor of being in my wrestling holds and in my presence. This is your gift for being a good boy." These words came out of the blue, but after the model left, Abe had an orgasm like he had never remembered.

Afterward, these words haunted him. Why had they aroused him so? Not fully understanding, he would ask future wrestling sex workers to say this to him, but it was never the same as when this particular man said it spontaneously. He compulsively returned for more contact with that sex worker and enjoyed being told he was a "good boy" the more he paid him.

What was this the erotic code in Abe's sexual behaviors and interest with these men? Why did the guys have to be straight? Why was paying them a part of what aroused him?

Abe had never been able to please his alcoholic father. His parents divorced when he was ten, and when he visited his father, the man would be watching sports on television and couldn't be easily pulled away. He constantly asked Abe to get him things, which Abe would do to please him. Abe recalls being frustrated with his father's greater allegiance to television and alcohol than to Abe himself.

When Abe's mother remarried, his stepfather ordered Abe around, making him do house chores. He asked for allowance and payment for the chores, but his stepfather gave him nothing, not even thanks or recognition. He recalls feeling much anger about this but dared not to say anything for fear of his mother and stepfather's disapproval.

Whenever someone pays for sex, the metaphor "paying for love" is the first thing I think of. Abe had to please his father by performing acts of servitude. He had longed for both his father and stepfather to express appreciation for the acts of service Abe provided but never received this. So in Abe's sexual fantasy, he was able to please his stand-in father, the bodybuilder, with servitude all over again—only this time, receiving recognition by the guy's willingness to recognize Abe for his work. In his fantasy, Abe won his father over and everyone was satisfied—dad and son. This is why the men had to be straight, like his father and stepfather. This fantasy allowed resolution from earlier pain in his life.

There was one other factor—the guys had to be big and strong. Why was this so important and the biggest turn-on for Abe? Abe had never been able to show his strength to his father or stepfather. He had to comply, take orders, and be subordinate and submissive. In his fantasy, he could sexualize his feelings of weakness and helplessness, when in reality, he was afraid of showing his strength and talking back. In fantasy, he could let himself feel powerless and remove the childhood pain that he'd felt at being forced into servitude. His obsession with muscular wrestlers was his unconscious attempt to seek out a stronger father figure.

Abe could feel the truth in this interpretation, though it's no cookie-cutter explanation for all who engage in this behavior. Everyone will be different in what the interpretation is for them. Once it *fits* you—and you will know if it does—you're ready to do the work that's waiting for you. For Abe, decoding his fantasy about pleasing straight men brought up unfinished business with his father and stepfather. His therapy work was now about focusing on his relationships with those father figures and reclaiming his buried feelings about how they treated him.

Abe began to consider talking to his father and his stepfather about his feelings from childhood. I encouraged this, as I saw it would benefit his healing. This helped Abe's search for a partner since he now understood the importance of a strong man. It opened up a whole new avenue for Abe to let himself attach romantically and sexually to gay men and feel real love for men who could return it. Talking to these paternal figures allowed him to reclaim his own strength as a gay man.

Many people have problems attaching deeply and romantically because in their childhoods one or both parents might have been depressed or portrayed themselves as sick, weak, or incompetent. Children are very sensitive to their parents' needs and in attempting to please them, will adapt to being less of a burden. In adulthood, this can lead to difficulties in being a "burden" to a potential partner and can be sexualized in a number of ways.

Objects of Passion

Objectification fantasies include fetishes and fantasies where body parts and objects are desired, rather than a whole person. I've heard clients fantasize about being a guy's footstool, table, chair, ashtray, or toilet; doing his chores, cleaning his house and car, and being totally humiliated and submissive to him. This can signify that while growing up, the gay male was treated poorly, like an object.

Again, as sexual fantasy and sexual play, there's nothing wrong with this if you enjoy it safely and sanely with those willing to participate. But in a relationship, then you need to somehow incorporate this sexual fantasy with a partner.

Bader writes, "People often use fetishes to become aroused. In these cases, the function of fetishes is to eliminate any guilt and worry that might interfere with sexual excitement by eliminating the *human* dimension of the other person." Doing so can remove any anxieties or concerns about truly connecting to another person and letting oneself have relational experiences.

Cam You See Me?

It's been said that the word intimacy breaks down as *into me you see*. While you can let some of yourself show over online with a Webcam, it's not the same form of intimacy that being face-to-face demands. Watching our culture—gay, bi and straight—become more computer-dependent, using the Internet for contact more and more, I fear that our skills for attachment and intimacy are starting to atrophy. Gay men from all over the country have told me how hard it is to socialize with other men to find Mr. Right. In many places, gay men are no longer even going to bars to find dating partners—they're logging on to the Internet.

Most men willing to show themselves on cams are going to be more confident about their looks and their bodies. For the most part, they have bigger penises, gym bodies, and average to better-than- average looks. This gives many gay men the impression that their partners should look something like this. Thanks to the display of men online, sexual attraction has become more narrowly defined.

Some gay men in my office and workshops seem very picky about the type of men they're looking for. Like women who see only photographs of slender Barbie-like models, gay males are moving in that direction too, and it's largely due to the Internet. Gay men are comparing themselves to the guys they see in still photos or on Webcams and saying, "What's wrong with me? I don't look like that! I'll never find a partner!" I tell them that men willing to display themselves in the buff are those who have larger endowments overall and feel better about their bodies. They're not necessarily men to measure yourself against.

Does HIV Really Have to Be the Price to Pay to Belong?

Jonathan came to me after struggling with sexual fidelity with his partner. He had been cheating for the past several years and finally had to admit it after becoming HIV-positive. He knew he was out of integrity but also knew that cheating on his partner was compelling and exciting. We explored his sexual behavior to decode what he was seeking through his compulsiveness.

Jonathan had never felt that he fit in anywhere and always had a desire to belong. Effeminate and overweight, he said, “gay men look right through me.” For sex, he went to bathhouses, on gay apps, and bottomed at sex parties where gay men took turns penetrating him without condoms. His one rule was not to let anyone ejaculate inside him. He refused to go on PrEP.

I asked what his peak erotic fantasy was and it was of men using him for their enjoyment by having anal sex with no protection. He wasn’t concerned about getting any sexual pleasure back from them.

His desire for acceptance and pleasing these men overshadowed his worries about HIV infection. In fact, it turned him on more that he was there for *them*—completely.

One time, a man was just about to orgasm, and Jonathan knew the man should pull out, but he didn't. At the moment, Jonathan didn't care. He knew it was wrong, but his urge to please this man was stronger than the urge to protect himself.

The man ejaculated inside him, and Jonathan recalls being sick several weeks after the incident. Later, he tested positive for HIV. Why would he have put himself at risk like this?

In his therapy, we uncovered his very strong need to be accepted and to belong by his peers. Jonathan grew up in an upper- middle-class neighborhood even though his parents could barely afford it. His status-conscious peers dressed better and he always stood out because his family could not buy for him the things his friends had and wore. He'd never felt accepted in his family who praised his older brother for his proficiency in sports and his sister for her excellent academic record. In school, he was excluded from the various cliques. Unable to achieve acceptance and community for himself, he found that being everyone's bottom at the baths and sex parties made him feel like he belonged.

Jonathan's therapy now centered around his finding a sense of acceptance and belonging in non-risky, nonsexual ways, such as volunteering at organizations to help other gay men, even those living with HIV. HIV was his wake-up call, but he wished he had gotten help sooner. Jonathan's story is important for anyone who can get help sooner rather than later, regardless of one's state of health.

Sometimes sexual abuse survivors engage in self-abusive behavior. Many theories seek to explain why sexual abuse survivors so often cut themselves with razors and other sharp objects. Research indicates that, among other things, they're trying to bring what feels so inwardly awful into outside pain. Also, they prefer to feel present-tense pain related to a new injury rather than the lingering emotional injury from past sexual abuse.

Again, our gay male culture is forced to experience hate and homophobia in the media and we gay men experience it personally on a daily basis—even if it is not directed at us personally. Religions condemn us. In the United States, we can still be excluded from housing and jobs with little to no legal recourse. The result is that we become our own oppressors, via the self-abuse and self-injury that I see manifesting in barebackers and self-identified bug-chasers and gift- givers.

I've listened to men involved in both these dangerous practices and always see them as forms of self-cutting and abuse. It is like the childhood abuse survivor unconsciously saying, "See how damaged I am? You don't believe me? I'll show you" and revealing his scars for everyone to see. Those seeking to contract HIV say they are looking for a sense of belonging—a sort of brotherhood or community that they can't find in other ways. Sadly, they're looking for it in the sexual shadows.

But of course, they don't frame it that way. Some men say, "I want to get the virus. It relieves me of the anxiety of worrying about getting it." Others say, "I should be able to bareback. Sex was taken away from me once by those against my homosexuality, and they're not going to take it from me now. I'm not going to deaden my pleasure with latex." Statements like this are cries for help especially now that we have PrEP. Wanting to belong at the cost of something that can kill us is a trauma response from the abuse we gay men endure.

The Gift That Keeps On Giving

The Case of Terry

Terry was always paying for sex when he would travel for his job, which he did on a regular basis. He was not taking PrEP. One time, he was receiving anal sex from an escort who purposely removed his condom right before ejaculating. Terry knew it happened since he felt the wetness running down his thighs. He was frozen in shock, as the escort put his clothes back on and left in silence. Neither said a word.

Terry had been living with this for one year now. For therapeutic reasons, I asked Terry to write the escort an angry letter, but not mail it. (He wouldn't be able to find the guy's address anyway.) I wanted him to read the letter aloud, but he wanted me to read it instead. He said he did not want to cry and wanted to distance himself from his feelings because this was so hard for him. So I read it aloud.

Letter to Gift-Giver Perpetrator:

You won't remember me.

We had a brief encounter in my hotel room last summer. Our meeting was probably nothing out of the ordinary for you—you must have many such encounters in your line of work—but it changed my life.

You infected me with HIV, and I have to believe you meant to.

Our encounter had been safe right up to the point when you deliberately removed our protection. After six weeks, I had the symptoms of acute HIV infection and was diagnosed as positive.

Since then, I've been holding myself to blame: I was a consenting partner, aware of the risks with someone I'd met on the Internet, and had taken such risks for some time. Maybe my luck was bound to run out.

On reflection, though, that's too easy. The fact is, on my other encounters, the play was always safe. So why did you remove our protection? Was it just recklessness on your part, a wish to play dangerously? I think you knew you were positive and had every intention of passing on the virus. But either way, what you did was wrong, and had the same consequences I now have to live with.

I can't change what happened, but believe me, I agonize over how it did. For a brief physical pleasure that would otherwise be soon forgotten, I must suffer the memory of how easily and cheaply you cut my life expectancy. For the time I have left (hopefully years, not months) I will suffer a reduced quality of life to protect my health. I may never find a life partner. Perhaps worst of all, what will this do to my family and friends?

Were these thoughts going through your head when you went out of your way to infect me? Did someone pass the virus to you in a similar way? And therefore, drive you to seek revenge on others? I can only imagine this is the retribution you sought.

How easy it must be to become a victim, blaming everyone but yourself and making a career (literally) out of passing on the infection. But you have to stop. You have to get the anger out of you and stop the chain of suffering. I am trying to find room in my heart for forgiveness, trying hard to control my anger and act responsibly towards others and not become a risk to them in the way you were to me.

I guess I'll never know your reasons or what became of you. It's ironic that you won't remember me, and I will never be able to forget you.

After I read this—with tears in my eyes—Terry said it was actually worse having me read it and him having to hear it. But it did put him in touch with feelings that he wasn't able to access before the session.

Homo-Work on Changing Your Erotic Code

1. What is your peak erotic fantasy?

2. What sexual fantasies do you *like* and *dis*like the most?

3. Which of your sexual fantasies have you never told a soul about, not even your partner—and which you might not have admitted even to yourself?

4. What physical type of men are you attracted to sexually?

5. What type of porn do you look at most? Vanilla, kink, role- playing, solo, threesomes, or orgies?

____

6. Are you the sexual pursuer or the pursued—even in fantasy and on the Internet? What are your most enjoyable sexual positions?

____

____

____

7. How do you feel about your body, particularly your penis size?

____

____

____

8. Can you enjoy sex—both receiving and giving—with your partner?

____

____

____

References

Dawn Atkins, ed., *Looking Queer* (New York: Harrington Park Press, 1998).

Michael Bader, *Arousal: The Secret Logic of Sexual Fantasies* (New York: St. Martin's Press, 2002).

Guy Kettelhack, *Dancing Around the Volcano* (New York: Crown, 1996).

Joe Kort, "Gay Men and Their Porn," *In the Family* (Summer 2002).

Jack Morin, *The Erotic Mind: Unlocking the Inner Sources of Sexual Passion and Fulfillment* (New York: HarperPerennial, 1996).

Frank Sanello, *Tweakers: How Crystal Meth Is Ravaging Gay America* (Los Angeles: Alyson Books, 2005).

Published by Smart Sex-Smart Love Books